EASY DOES IT® for Apraxia and Motor Planning

Robin Strode
Catherine Chamberlain

LinguiSystems

LinguiSystems, Inc.
3100 4th Avenue
East Moline, IL 61244

1-800-PRO IDEA
1-800-776-4332

FAX: 1-800-577-4555
E-mail: service@linguisystems.com
Web: www.linguisystems.com
TDD: 1-800-933-8331
(for those with hearing impairments)

Skill Area:	Apraxia and Motor Planning
Interest Level:	Ages 4 thru 12

Printed in the U.S.A.
ISBN 1-55999-264-6

About the Authors

Robin M. Strode, M.A., CCC-SLP, has had 20 years experience as a speech-language pathologist. She has been in private practice for 12 years. In addition to her private practice, Robin has served as a school consultant and a part-time instructor in the Communication Disorders Department at the University of Kentucky. She formerly worked in the public schools for eight years. During that time, she began a pilot self-contained class for children with severe language disorders. Robin has a special interest in working with preschool and early elementary-aged children with developmental delays, language disorders, and/or speech disorders. *Easy Does It for Apraxia and Motor Planning* is Robin's second publication with LinguiSystems.

Catherine E. Chamberlain, M.A., CCC-SLP, maintains a private practice serving three- to fifteen-year-olds. In addition to her private practice, Catherine works in the summers at the Early Childhood Development Center in Winchester, Kentucky. Catherine was formerly a speech-language pathologist and diagnostician in the Fayette County school system for 14 years. Catherine has also served on curriculum development teams and as a school consultant. She has a special interest in working with students with autism, mental disabilities, and multiple handicaps. *Easy Does It for Apraxia and Motor Planning* is Catherine's fourth publication with LinguiSystems.

April 1993

Dedication

To my friends at the Early Childhood Development Center, young and young at heart, past and present, especially Steven and his wonderful mother, Evelyn. To Tom and Cole, who make my life so special. — Robin

To the children who teach us as much as we teach them. And, as always, to my home team. — Catherine

Laura Cherf: Editor
Bonnie Duckett: Graphic Designer
Jennifer Kay: Desktop Publisher
Laura Sauser: Editorial Assistant
Margaret Warner: Artist

Table of Contents

Table of Contents

Goal 6

The Long Vowel Team

Meet the long vowel team members.

5

Vowel Trading Cards

Use these cards to teach vowel sounds and their hand signals. Descriptions for the hand signals are in Appendix B.

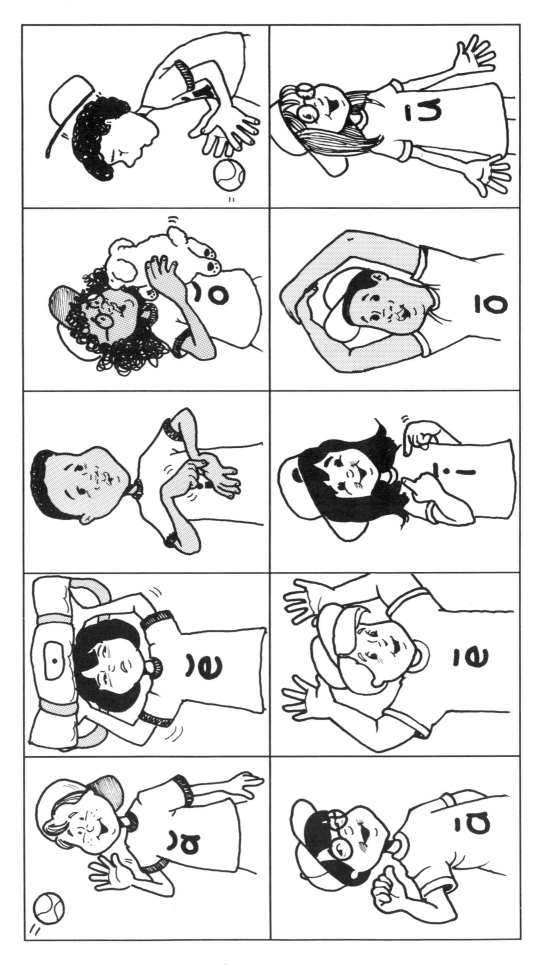

The Short Vowel Team

Meet the short vowel team members.

7

Pitching Practice

Say hello to the teams. Then, practice throwing the ball!

8

Play Practice

Move around the bases as you practice your sounds!

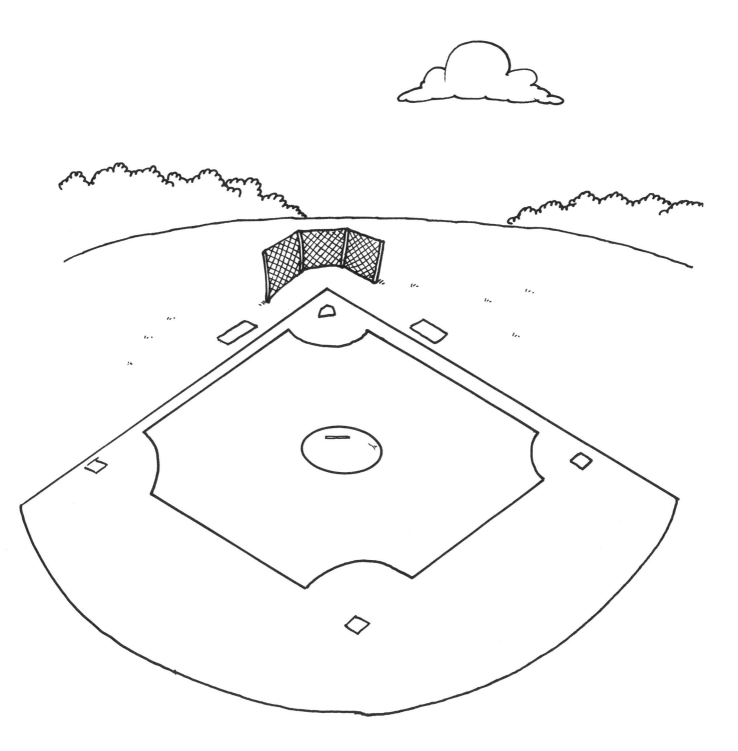

Consonant Trading Cards

Use these cards to teach consonants and their hand signals. Use the picture symbols as added cues for teaching consonant sounds. Descriptions of hand signals are in Appendix B.

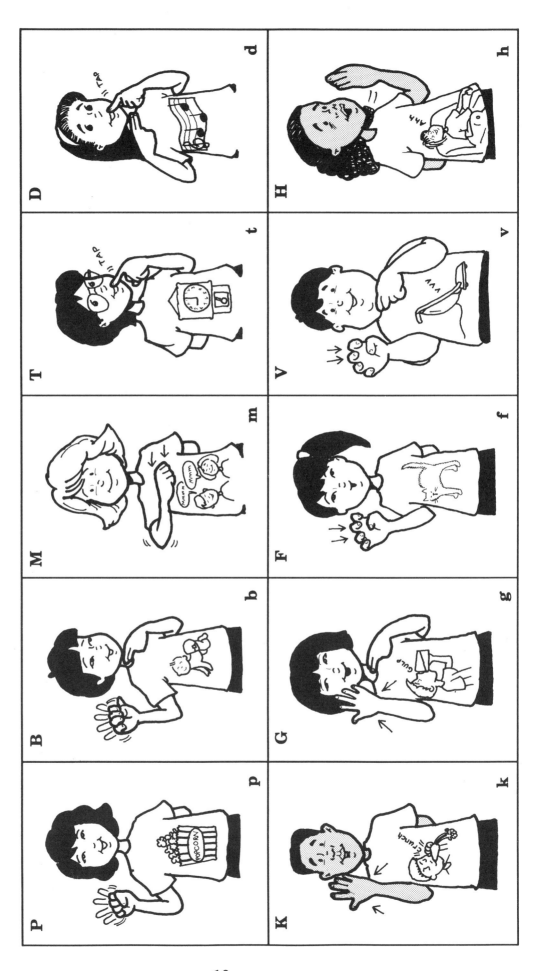

Consonant Trading Cards

Use these cards to teach consonants and their hand signals. Use the picture symbols as added cues for teaching consonant sounds. Descriptions of hand signals are in Appendix B.

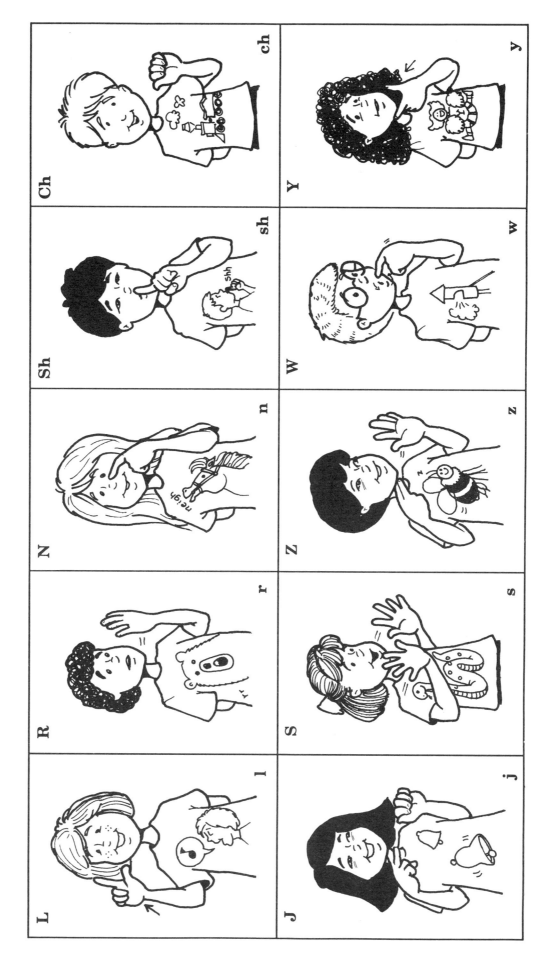

Consonant Rows

Touch each letter as you practice saying the sound.

p p p p p p p p

Place the *p* trading card.	Place the *b* trading card.

b b b b b b b b

Consonant Rows

Touch each letter as you practice saying the sound.

t   t   t   t   t   t   t   t

Place the *t* trading card.	Place the *d* trading card.

d   d   d   d   d   d   d   d

Consonant Rows

Touch each letter as you practice saying the sound.

m　m　m　m　m　m　m

Place the *m* trading card.	Place the *n* trading card.

n　n　n　n　n　n　n

Consonant Rows

Touch each letter as you practice saying the sound.

f   f   f   f   f   f   f   f   f

Place the *f* trading card.	Place the *v* trading card.

v   v   v   v   v   v   v   v

Consonant Rows

Name _____

Touch each letter as you practice saying the sound.

k　k　k　k　k　k　k　k

Place the *k* trading card.	Place the *g* trading card.

g　g　g　g　g　g　g　g

Consonant Rows

Touch each letter as you practice saying the sound.

S S S S S S S S S

Place the *s* trading card.	Place the *z* trading card.

Z Z Z Z Z Z Z Z Z

Consonant Rows

Touch each letter as you practice saying the sound.

sh   **sh**   **sh**   **sh**   **sh**   **sh**

ch   **ch**   **ch**   **ch**   **ch**   **ch**

Place the *sh* trading card.	Place the *ch* trading card.	Place the *j* trading card.

j   **j**   **j**   **j**   **j**   **j**   **j**   **j**   **j**

Consonant Rows

Touch each letter as you practice saying the sound.

l l l l l l l l l l

Place the *l* trading card.	Place the *r* trading card.

r r r r r r r r r

Consonant Rows

Name _____

Touch each letter as you practice saying the sound.

w w w w w w w

Place the *w* trading card.	Place the *y* trading card.

y y y y y y y

Consonant Rows

Name _____

Touch each letter as you practice saying the sound.

h   h   h   h   h   h   h   h

Place the *h* trading card.

Practice Pyramid

Practice your sounds as you climb the pyramid!

Knock Them Down

Knock all the shapes down by saying the sound on each shape.

23

Front Team Jacket

Name —————

Here's your team jacket! You'll glue a badge on your jacket each time you finish a sporting event.

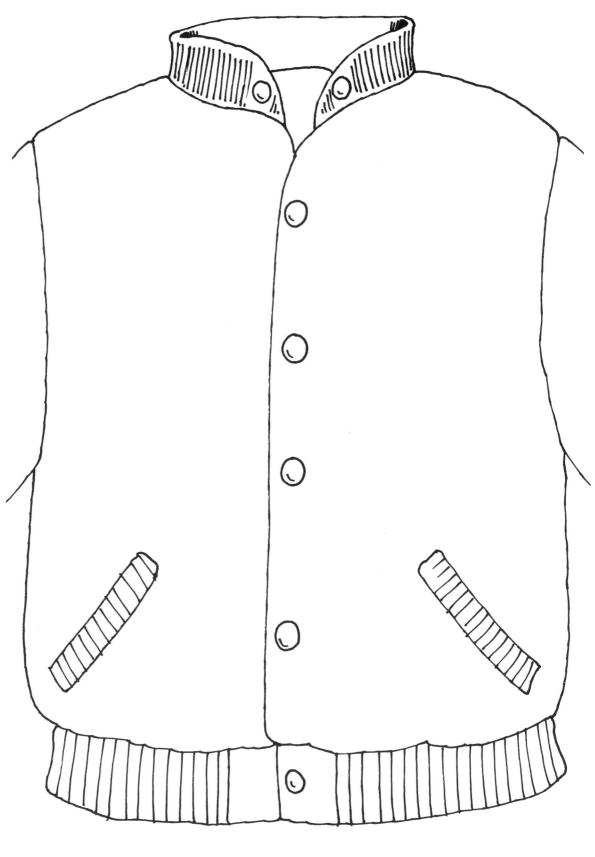

Back Team Jacket

Name _____

Here's the back of your team jacket! When the front is full, you'll glue a badge on the back of your jacket each time you finish your sporting event.

Badges

Badges

BASKETBALL

BADMINTON

VAULTING

ARCHERY

MINI
GOLF

BARS

HORSEBACK
RIDING

BASEBALL

SAILING

JACKS

BIKING

ICE-SKATING

Badges

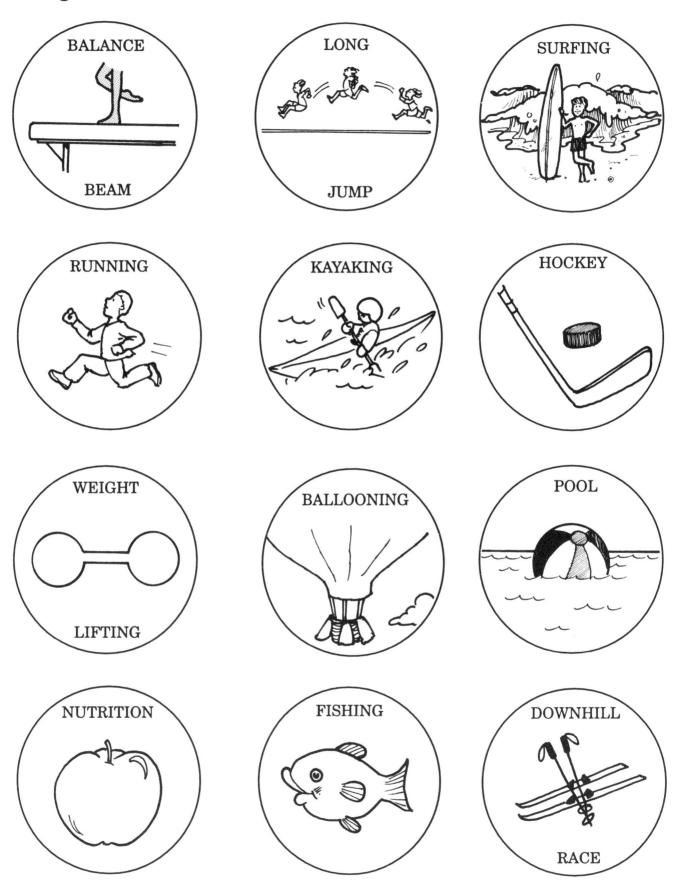

Badges

Badges

To the Top

Say each syllable as you move your teammate up and down each rope.

Over the Hurdles

Say each syllable as you move your teammate back and forth over the hurdles.

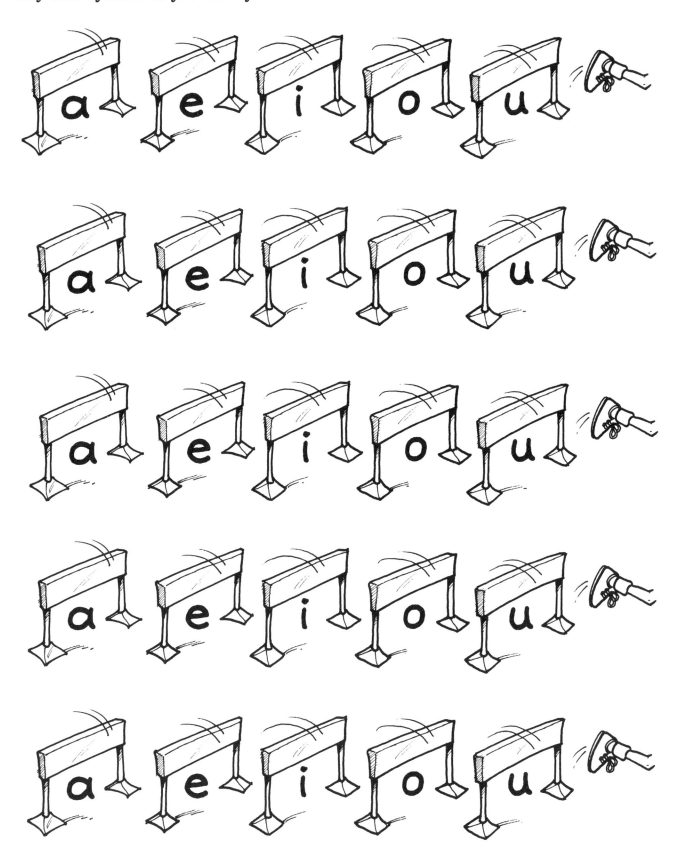

Ring Swing

Get in the swing!   Say each syllable five times!

Climb the Mountain

Name _____

Say your syllables as you climb to the top of the mountain.

Jump Rope

Say your syllables as you jump rope.

Chin-Ups

Continue your workout by saying your syllables as you do chin-ups.

Beanbag Toss

Throw your beanbag through the hole by saying the syllable sequences on each board.

Vowel Target Board

ă ĕ ĭ ŏ ŭ

ā ē ī ō ū

37

Tumbling

Complete the tumbling routine by saying the syllable sequences.

Vowel Scoreboard

ā ē ī ō ū
ă ĕ ĭ ŏ ŭ

Bowling

Get a strike! Say your syllable sequences on your way down the alley.

39

Consonant Syllables

pa	pe	pi	po	pu
ba	be	bi	bo	bu
ma	me	mi	mo	mu
ta	te	ti	to	tu
da	de	di	do	du
ka	ke	ki	ko	ku
ga	ge	gi	go	gu
sha	she	shi	sho	shu
cha	che	chi	cho	chu
ja	je	ji	jo	ju

Consonant Syllables

na	ne	ni	no	nu
ha	he	hi	ho	hu
wa	we	wi	wo	wu
fa	fe	fi	fo	fu
va	ve	vi	vo	vu
sa	se	si	so	su
za	ze	zi	zo	zu
ya	ye	yi	yo	yu
la	le	li	lo	lu
ra	re	ri	ro	ru

Make the Play

Score a touchdown by practicing all the syllable sequences on the football field.

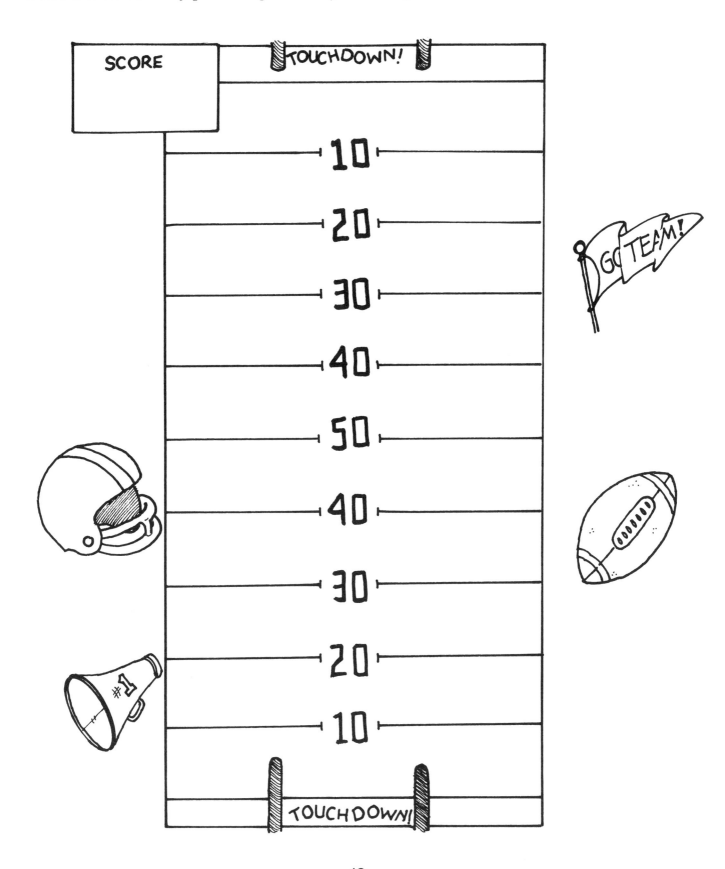

Tennis Anyone?

Keep the ball in play by practicing real and nonsense words.

Tennis Practice Rackets

Name _____

Use these rackets with the *Tennis Anyone?* worksheet.

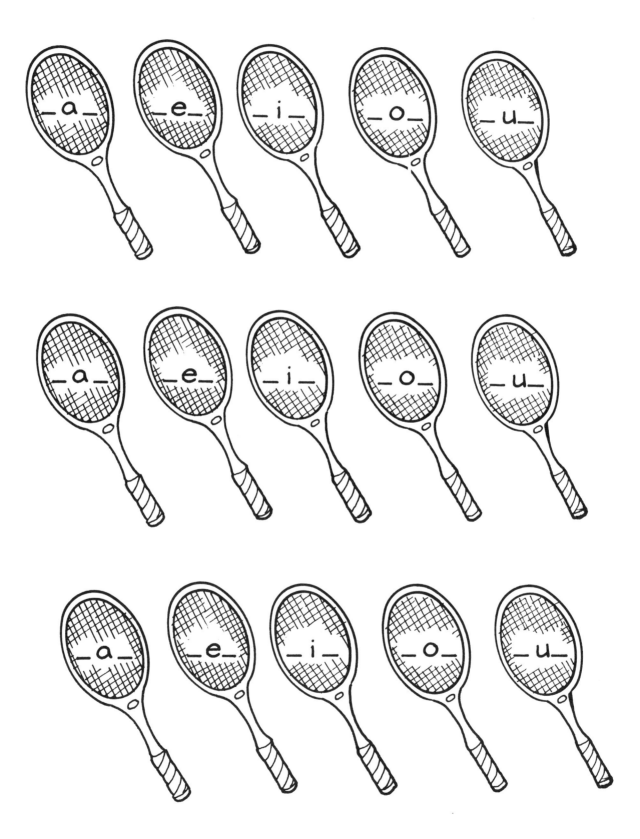

Push-Up Power

How many push-ups can you do? Practice saying the words above each athlete.

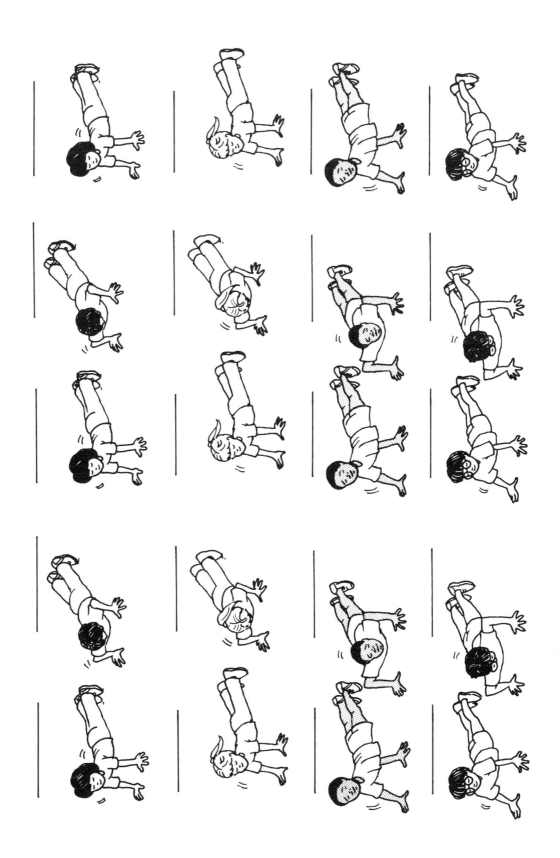

The Locker Room

Listen to the words your teacher says. Then, put your gym bags under the right door.

Gym Bags

Use these gym bags with *The Locker Room* worksheet.

Let's Play HORSE

Name _____

How many games can you win? Say the words on the basketballs.

scoreboard

H   O   R   S   E

Badminton Birdies

Practice your badminton skills by saying the words on the birdies.

Complete the Vault

Name _____

Practice saying words as you vault.

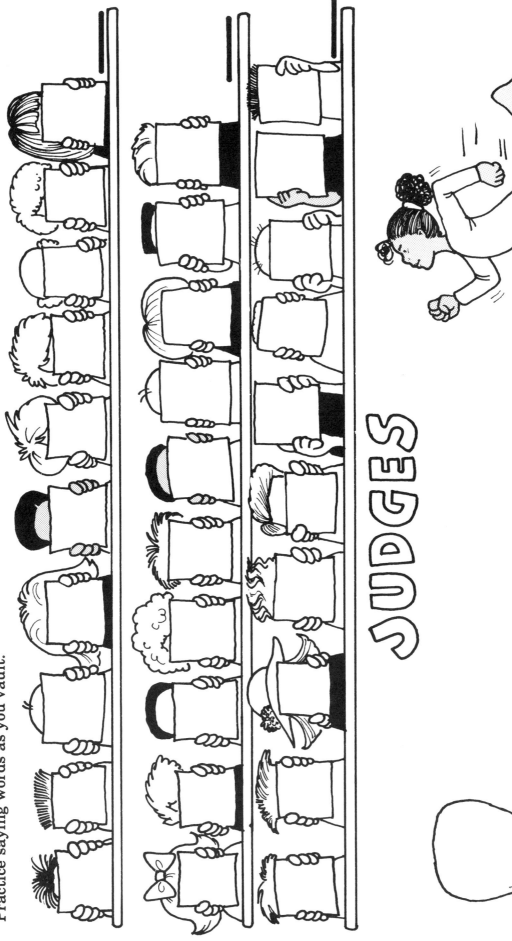

JUDGES

Hit the Bull's-Eye

Name _____

Hit the target by saying the words in the feathers.

Mini Golf

Name —————

Make a hole in one! Practice saying the words on the flags.

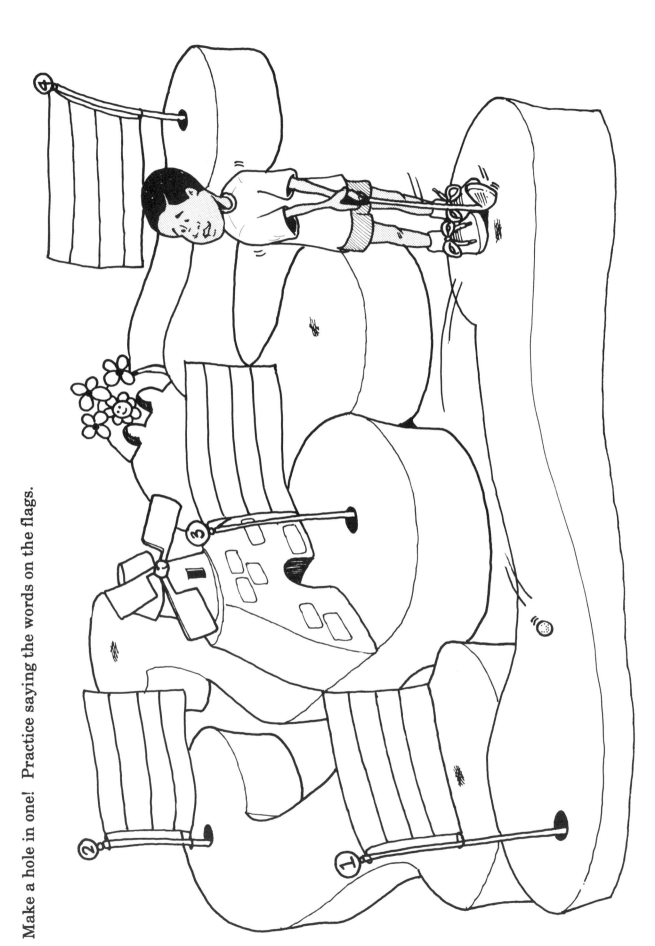

Sticking the Landing

"Stick the landing" by saying your words correctly!

Scorecard

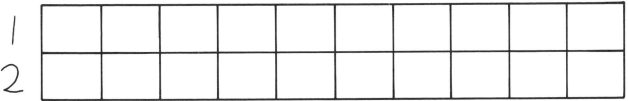

1
2

Scorecard

1
2

53

Complete the Course

Clear each jump by saying the words correctly.

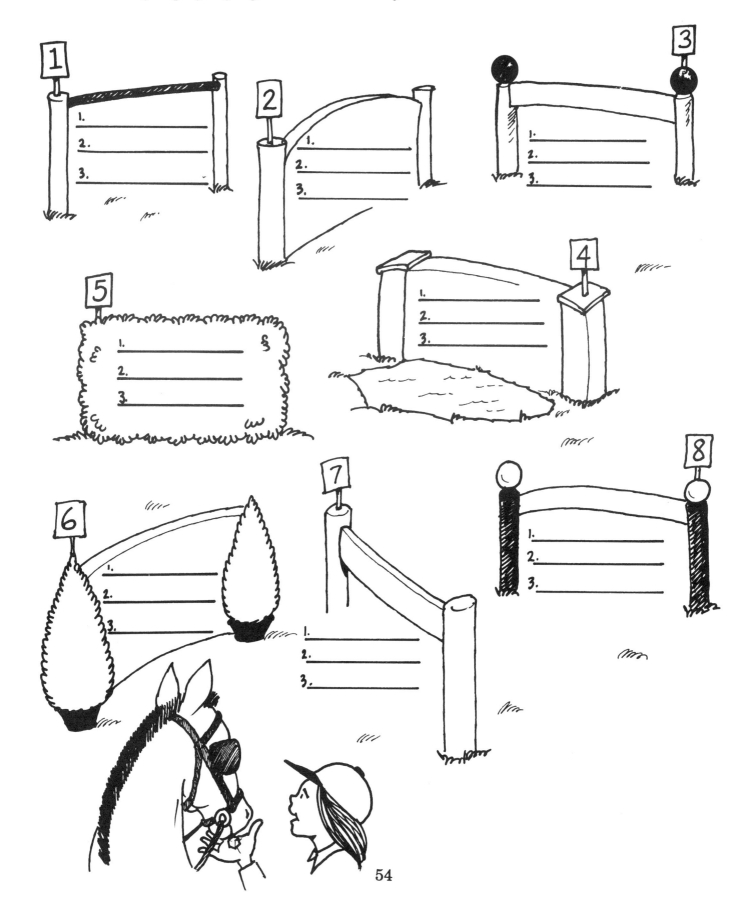

Play Ball

How many points can your team get? Practice saying your words and move along the bases.

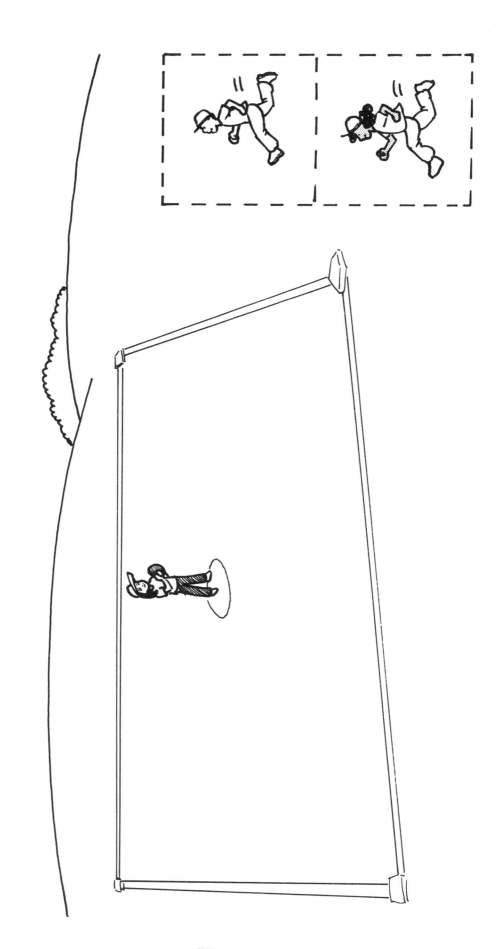

55

Baseballs

Use these baseballs with the *Play Ball* worksheet.

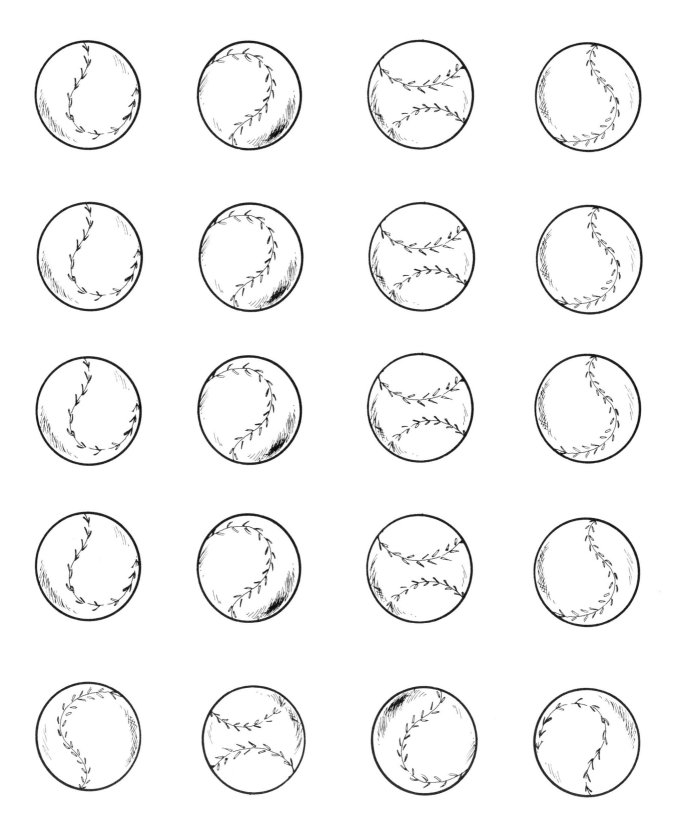

Sailing Race

Sail to the finish line by saying each word correctly.

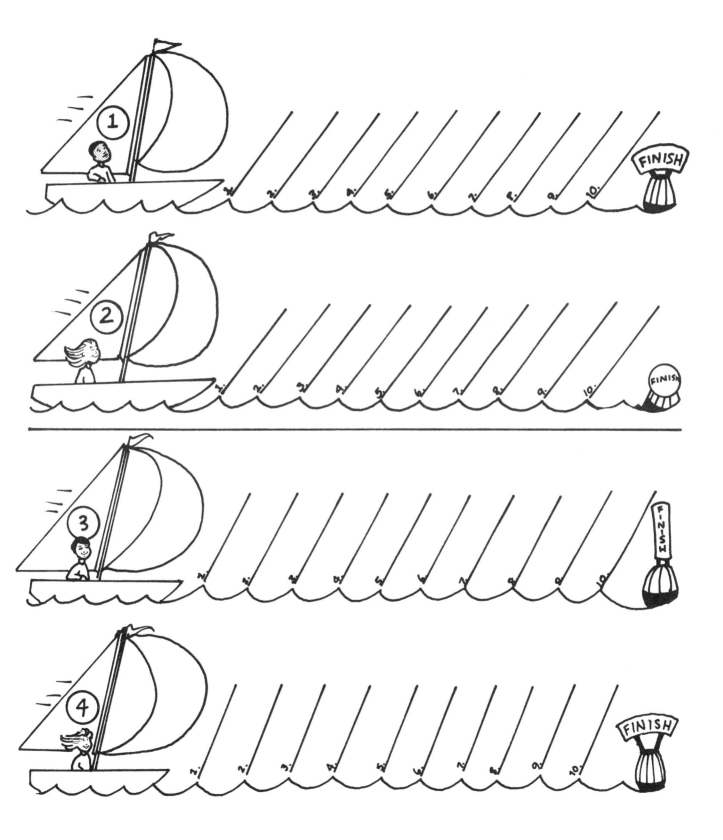

Let's Play Jacks

Practice saying your words as you play jacks.

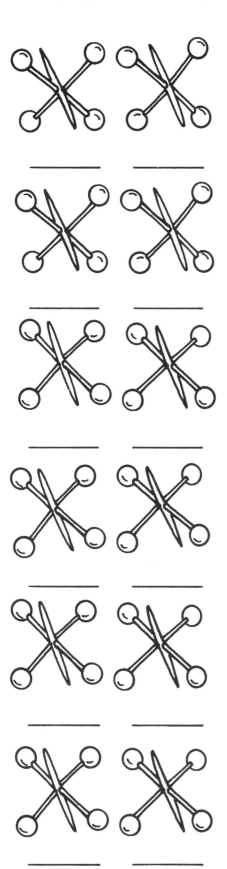

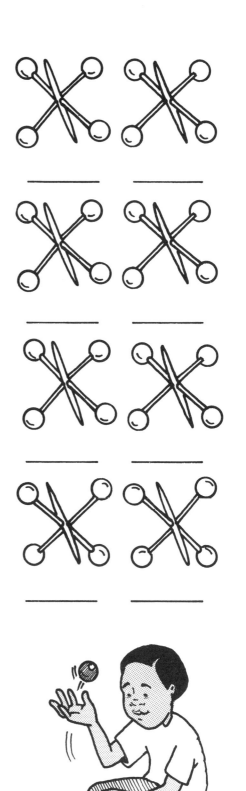

Bike Race

Practice each word to get to the finish line!

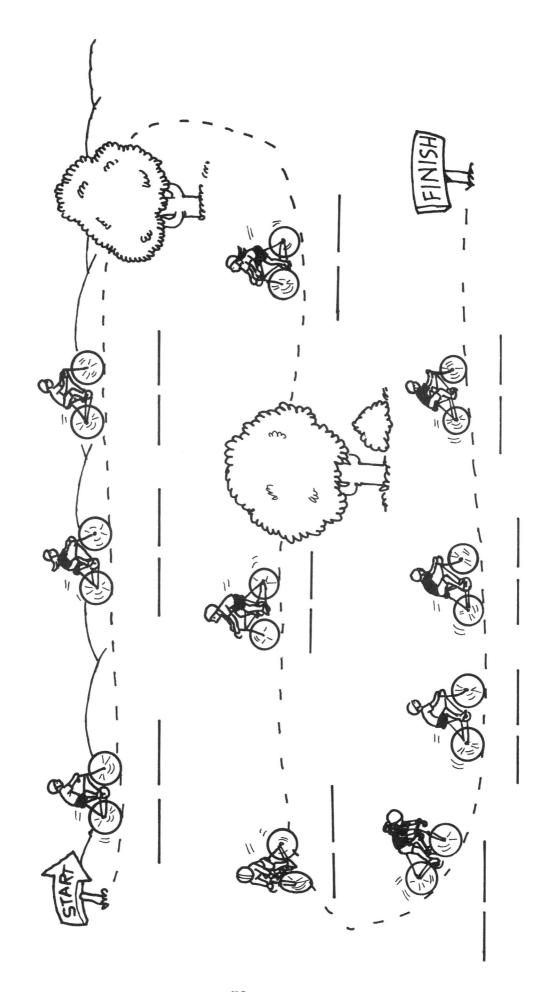

Ice-Skating

Score a perfect 10 by saying both syllables in each word!

Balancing Act

Complete the beam routine by saying all the syllables in each row.

Long Jump

Practice your long jump by saying your words.

Catch a Wave

Ride the waves to shore by saying each word correctly.

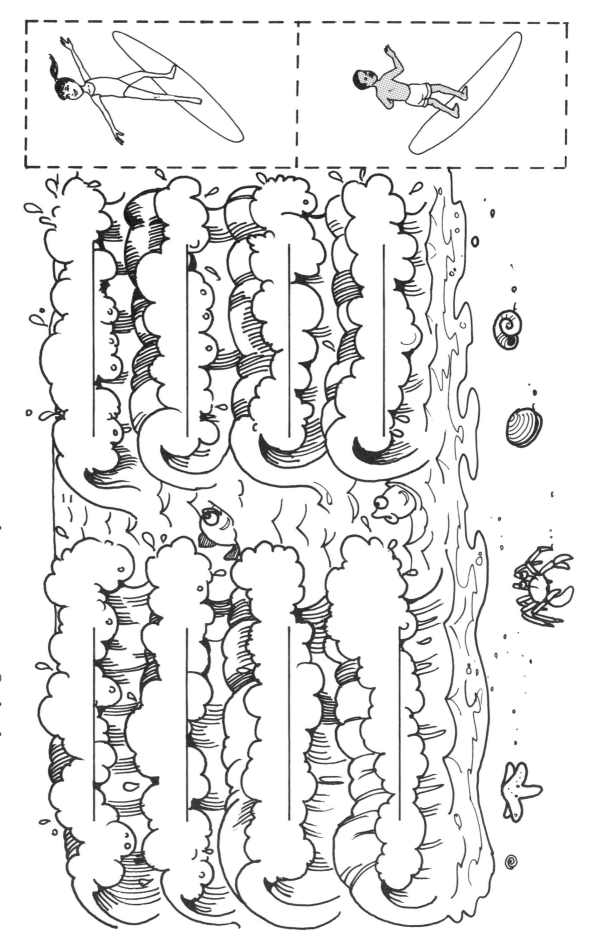

Name _____

Relay Race

Complete the race by saying all the words as you go around the track.

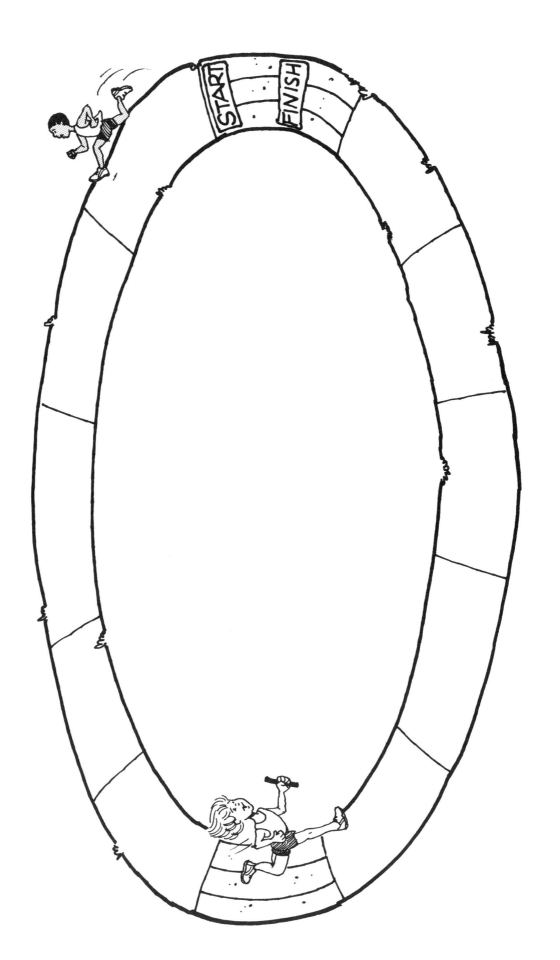

White Water Fun

Name _____

Finish the race by saying all the words correctly.

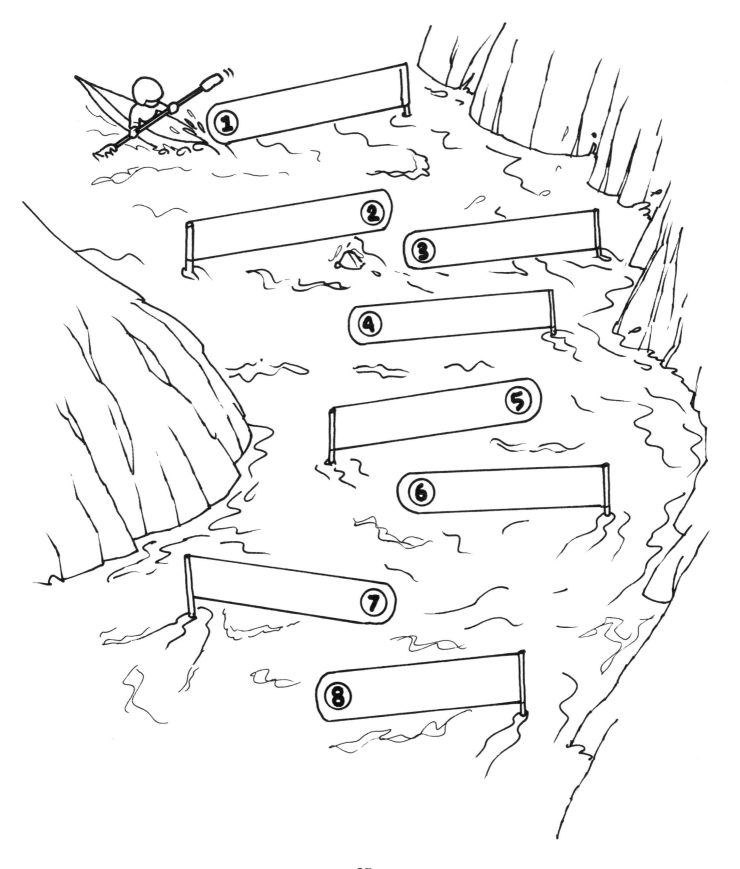

Passing the Puck

Score a goal by saying each word correctly.

Things I Want

Practice saying your phrases by telling what the boy wants.

67

Things I Can Do

Show what you can do by saying each phrase.

Three Cheers

Give the cheerleader something to cheer about. Say each of the phrases on the megaphones.

69

All About Me

Show off your medals by repeating each phrase.

_____

_____

_____

70

All About School

Practice the phrases on the hopscotch court to tell all about school!

Weights

Name _____

Use these weights with the *Weight Lifting* worksheet.

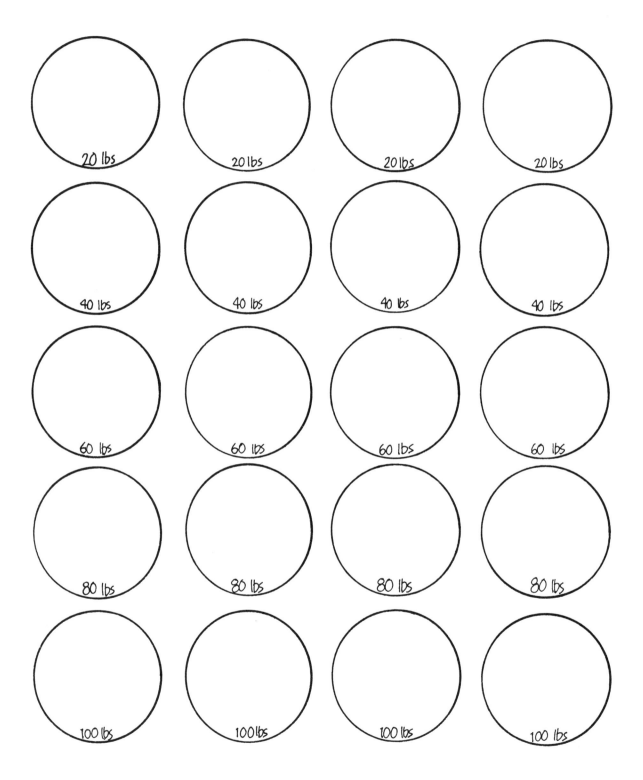

Weight Lifting

See if you can lift 100 pounds!

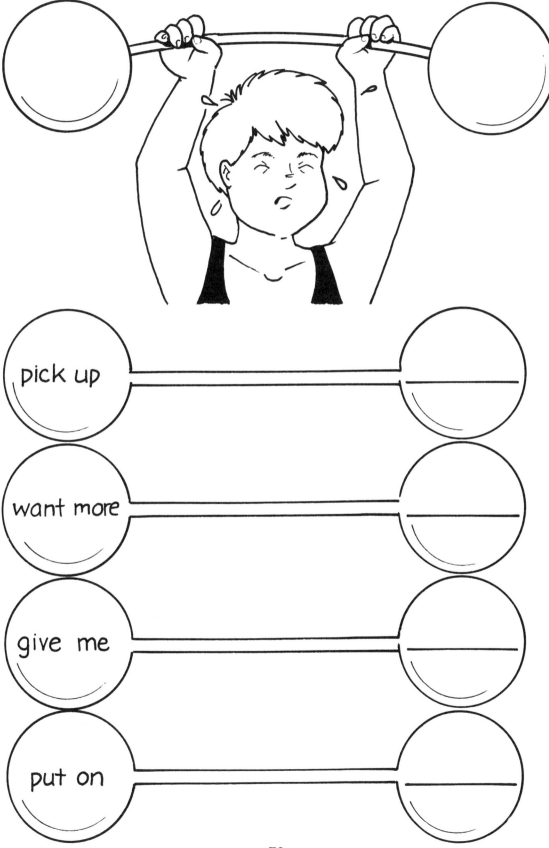

pick up

want more

give me

put on

Up, Up, and Away

Release the sandbags so you can fly. Say each phrase with the words on the hot air balloon.

74

Pool Game

Get the ball in the pocket each time you say a phrase with all five words.

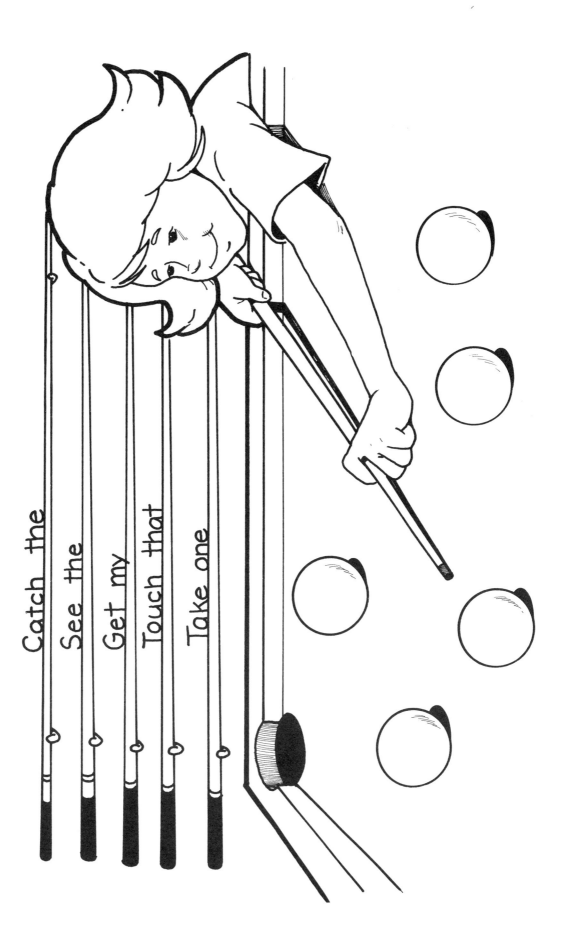

Catch the

See the

Get my

Touch that

Take one

Team Meal

Join the team for dinner! Practice each phrase with the words.

The Fishing Champ

Name _____

Win the fishing contest! Catch all the fish by saying the words on the fish with the
phrase on the bucket.

Fish

Use these fish with *The Fishing Champ* worksheet.

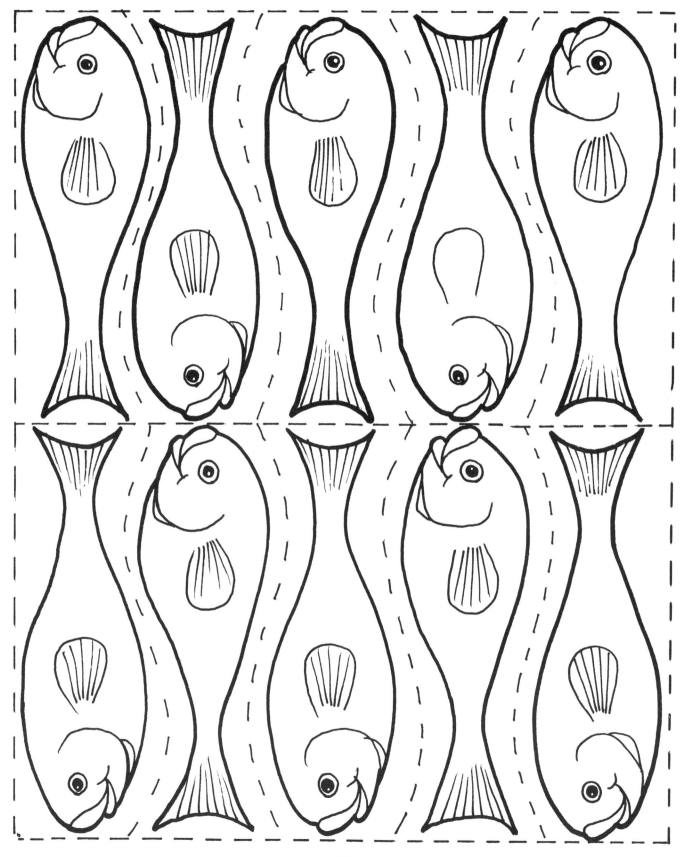

The Downhill Race

Name _____

Win the race by saying each sentence twice.

Frisbee Throw

Throw the frisbee 100 yards by practicing each phrase with each word to form a sentence.

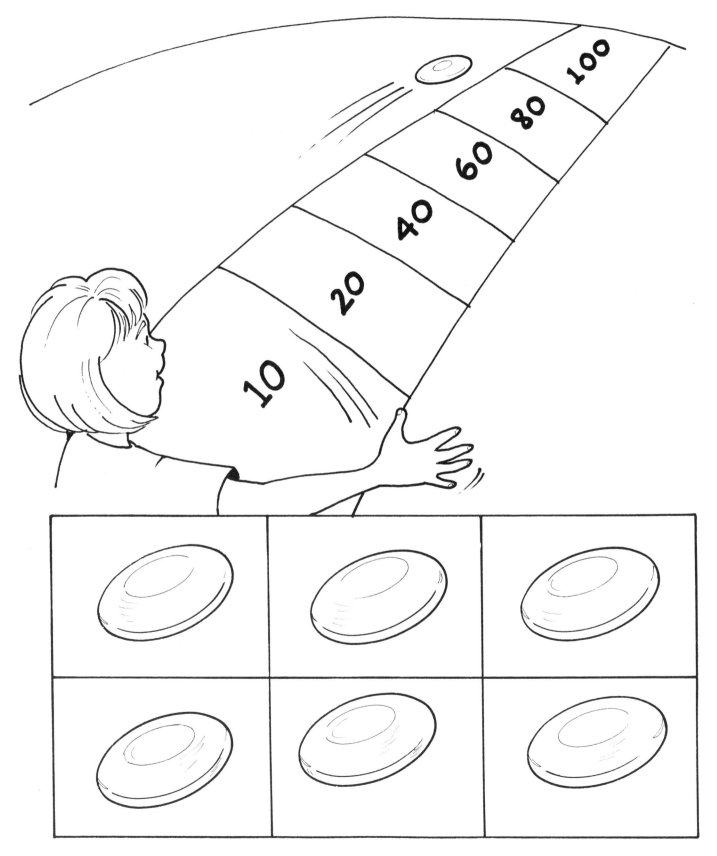

80

Shuffleboard

Get the most points and win the game by practicing each sentence.

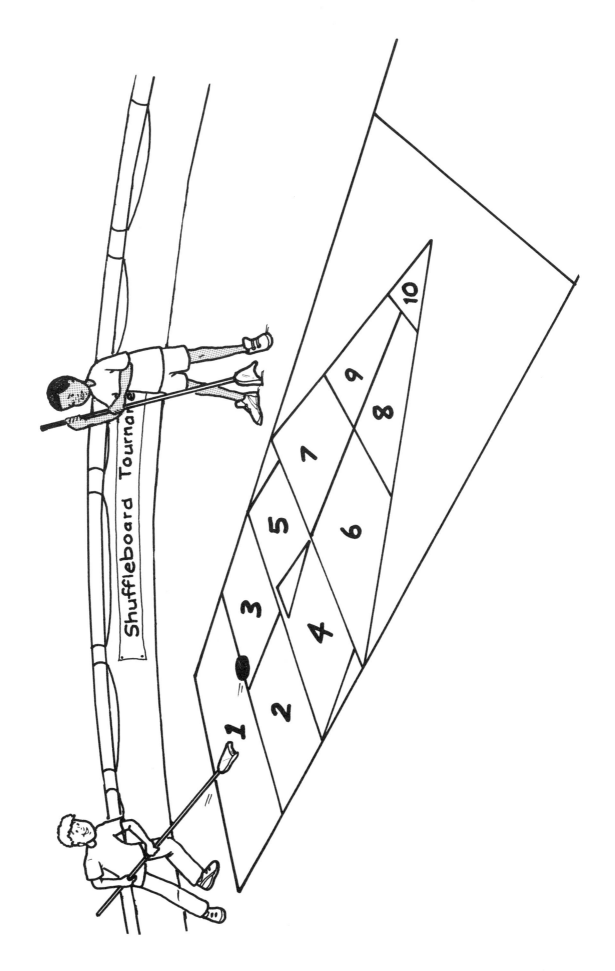

Scuba Diving

Practice each sentence as you dive!

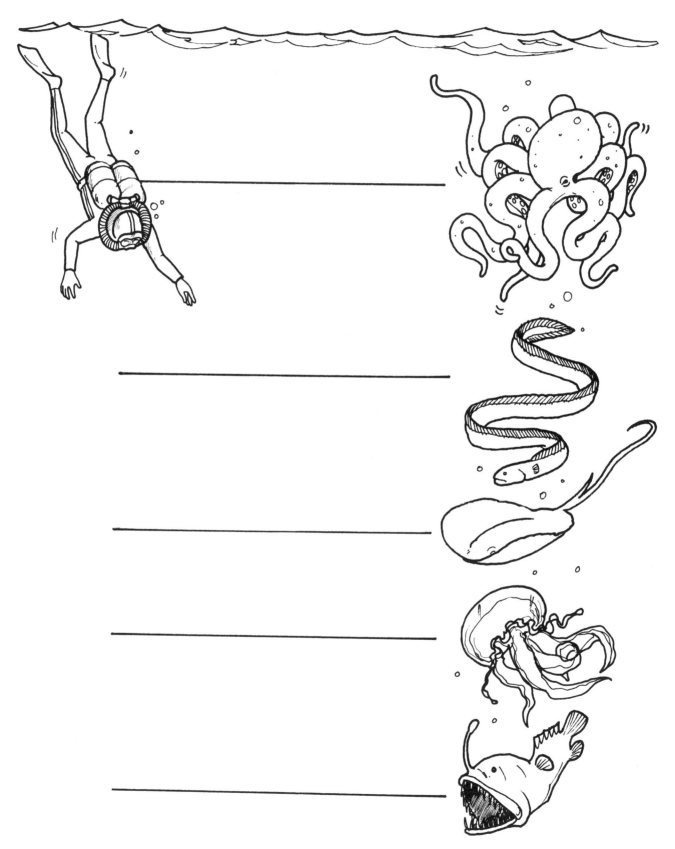

The Official Word

Name _____

Be an official! Practice the sentence on each whistle.

Official Whistles

Use these whistles with *The Official Word* worksheet.

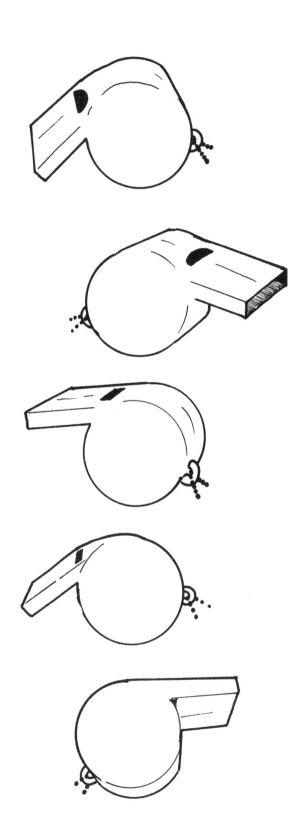

84

Sports Scrapbook

Answer each question about the pictures stressing the underlined words.

Sara is holding the horse.

Who is holding the horse?   What is Sara doing?
Is Sara holding the dog?

Linda made the last basket.

Who made the basket?   Did Linda miss the basket?
Did Linda make the first basket?

Ross hit the ball.

Who hit the ball?   Did Ross miss the ball?
Did Ross hit a ball?

Thomas won the race.

Who won the race?   Did Thomas lose the race?
Did Thomas win the golf game?

Jo held up the cup.

Who held up the cup?   Did Jo drop the cup?
Did Jo hold up his helmet?

Pete jumped over the bar.

Who jumped over the bar?   Did Pete climb
over the bar?   Did Pete jump over the mat?

Interview the Coach

Finish the interview by answering the questions and stressing the underlined words.

Jed threw the discus far.

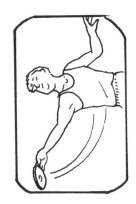

Who threw the discus?
<u>Did</u> Jed drop the discus?
Did Jed <u>throw</u> the Frisbee?

Tanya vaulted over the bar at 8 feet.

Who vaulted over the bar?
<u>Did</u> Tanya vault under the bar?
Did Tanya vault over the bar at <u>10</u> feet?

John won the 50-yard dash.

Who won the 50-yard dash?
<u>Did</u> John lose the 50-yard dash?
Did John win the <u>100</u>-yard dash?

Rose was happy with her Frisbee throw.

Who was happy?
<u>Was</u> Rose sad?
Was Rose happy with her <u>jump</u>?

Andy came in second in the long jump.

Who came in second?
<u>Did</u> Andy come in third?
Did Andy come in second in <u>swimming</u>?

Soccer Practice

Score a goal each time you practice a sentence.

87

Warm-Up Drills

Finish your warm-ups by practicing each sentence.

Today's Sports Report

Name _____

Present today's sports report by saying the sentences written under each picture.

Athlete of the Year

Name _____

Celebrate your accomplishments by practicing your sentences!

Springboard to Success

Name _____

Score a perfect ten for each diver by practicing the /s/ blend words.

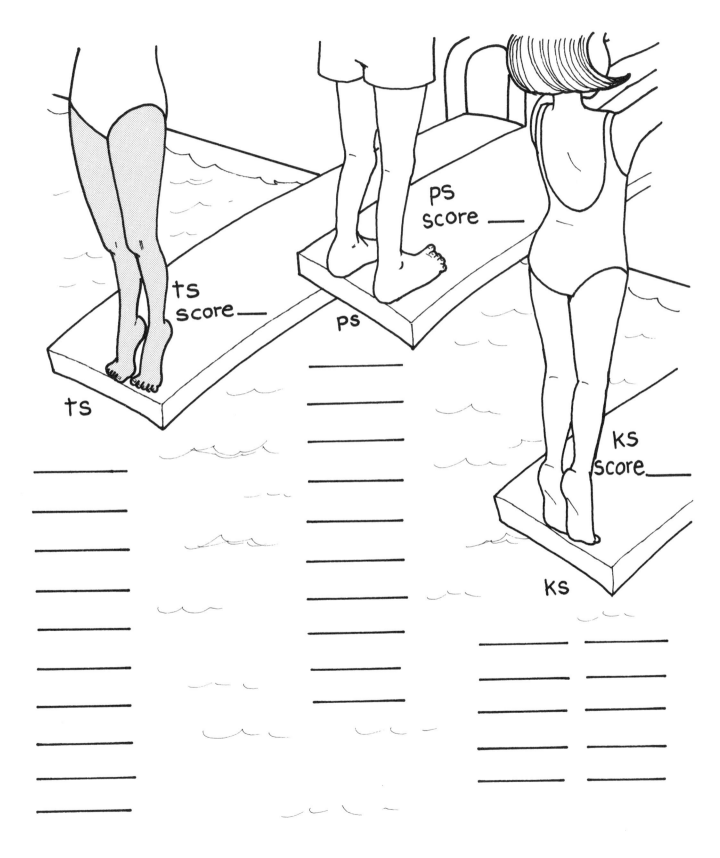

Off to Camp

Check your camping list by practicing each /s/ blend word.

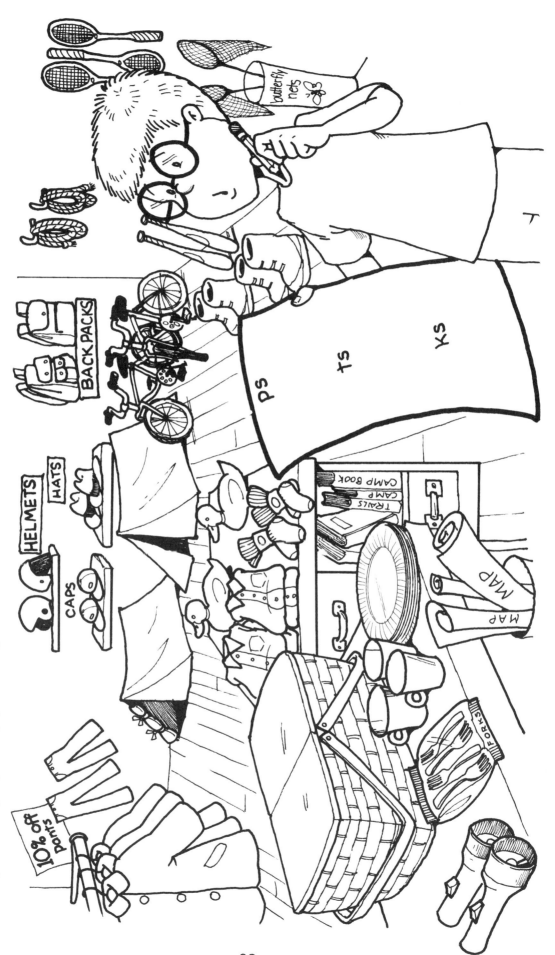

The Driving Range

Name _____

Stay in the "swing" by practicing all of the /s/ blend words.

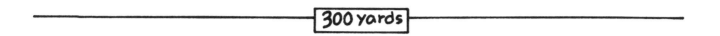

300 yards

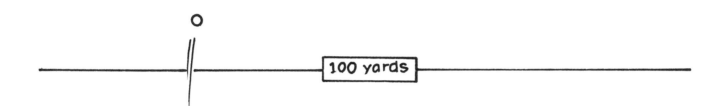

200 yards

100 yards

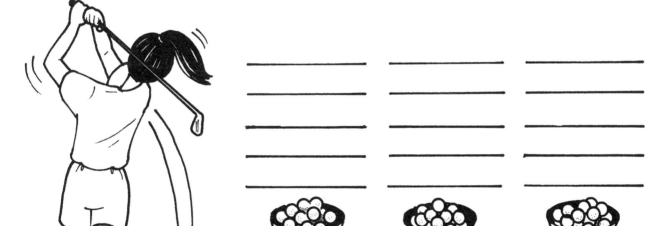

Playing Marbles

Knock each marble out of the circle by saying your /s/ blend words.

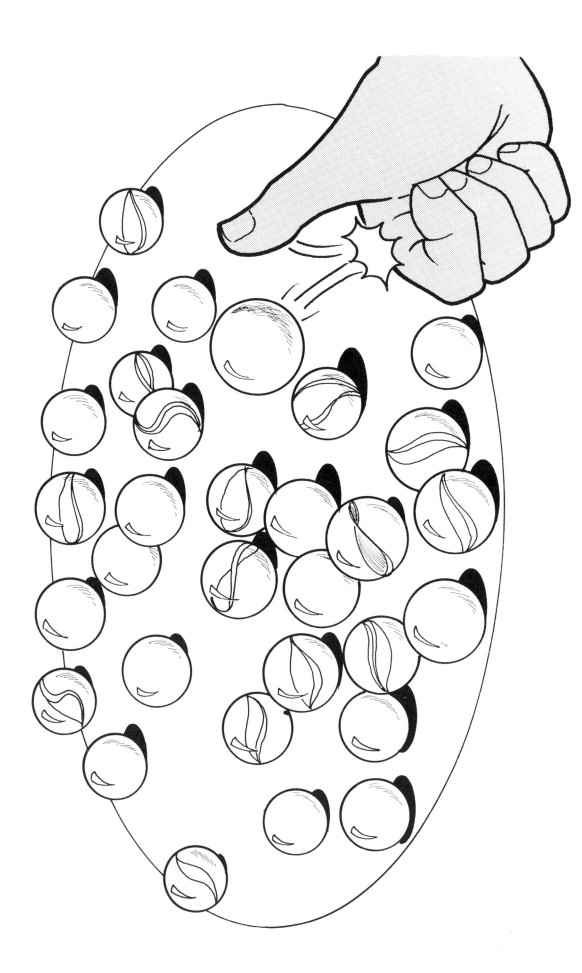

94

Ski the Moguls

Ski the moguls by practicing each /s/ blend word.

Rappel Down Blend Mountain

Name _____

Rappel down the mountain as you say each /s/ blend word.

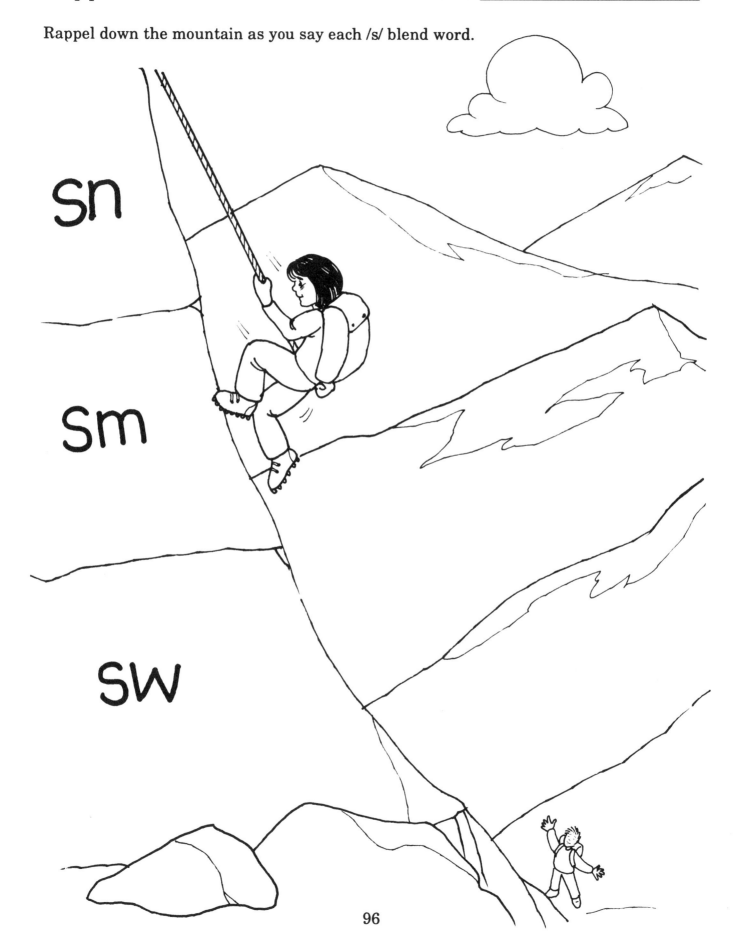

A Day of Sledding

Have fun sledding as you practice the /s/ blend words.

Water Ski Jumping Team

Ski over each jump by saying the words on each jump.

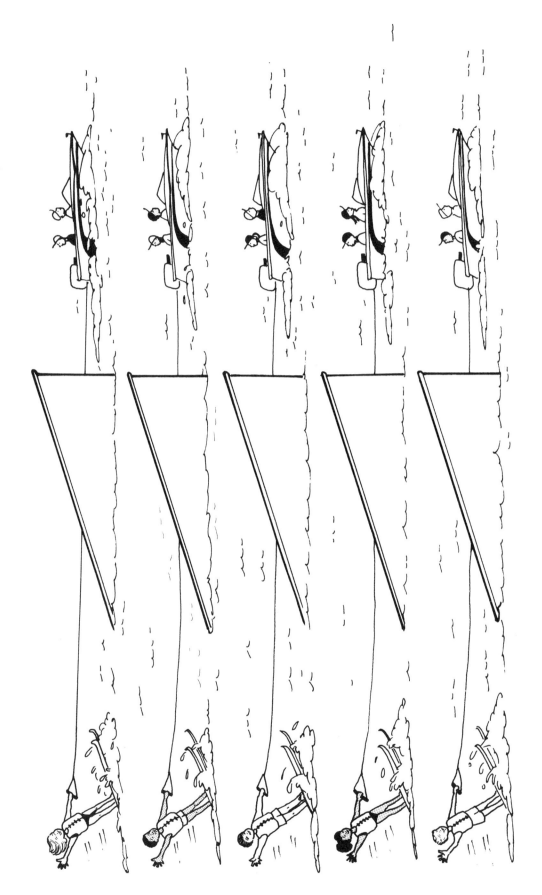

Jet Ski Fun

Practice for the race by saying the words on each buoy.

On the Mark

Help the swimming team practice by saying each /l/ blend word twice.

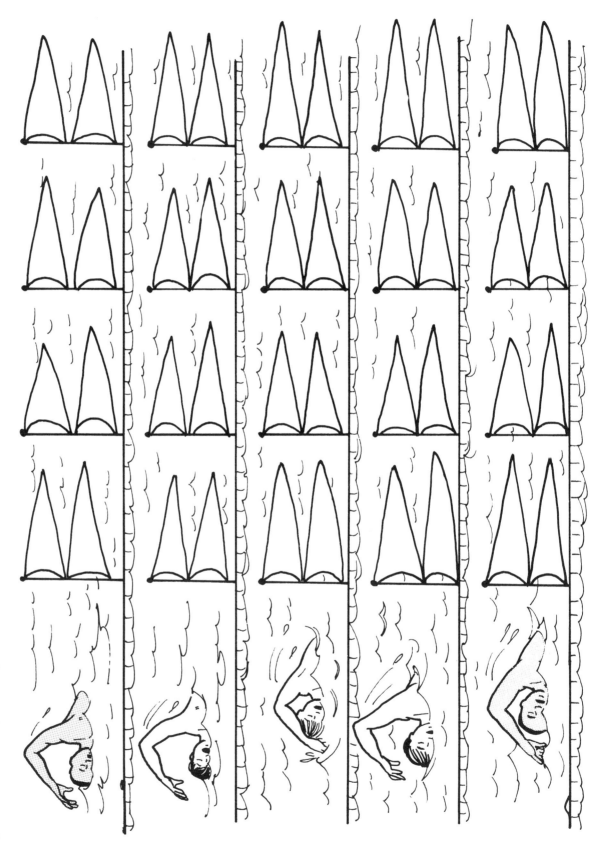

Horseshoes

How many points can you earn by saying each word correctly?

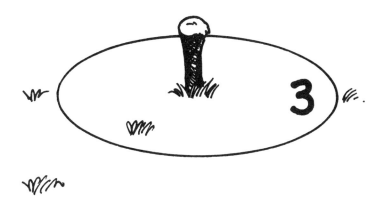

3

1

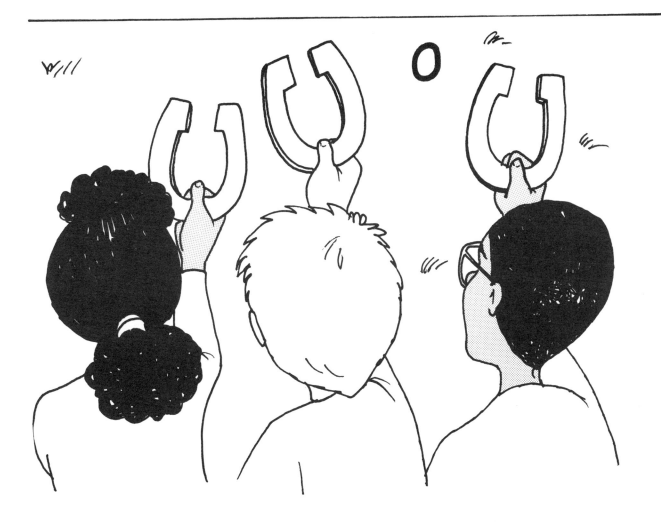

0

The Takedown

Score four takedowns by saying the words in front of each wrestler.

Steady Steps

Climb to the top by practicing all the words on the mountain.

103

Matching Backpacks

Name _____

1-03-14